ABOUT THE AUTHOR

Geoffrey Thomas was born in Merthyr Tydfil, Wales, in 1938. He studied at Cardiff University and later trained for the ministry at Westminster Theological Seminary, Philadelphia. He spent fifty years as Pastor of Alfred Place Baptist Church, Aberystwyth and is the author of several books and numerous articles. He has published three other works of fiction with Reformation Lightning. Geoffrey Thomas was awarded an honorary doctorate from Westminster Theological Seminary in 2011. He lives in London.

The Legendary Casey Jones and Other American Folktales

The Emperor's New Clothes and Other Stories

The Pied Piper of Hamelin and Other Tales

THE BOY WHO SHOUTED "WOLF!" BUT THERE WASN'T A WOLF

AND OTHER FABLES

GEOFFREY THOMAS

Reformation
Lightning

Reformation Lightning

www.reformationlightning.com

First published by Reformation Lightning in 2021

ISBN 978-1-8381883-1-3
1 3 5 7 10 8 6 4 2

To my dear great-grandchildren—
Gwilym, Ezra, Macsen, Gruffydd and Betsan

CONTENTS

INTRODUCTION

One day two men were sent to put the Lord Jesus in prison. But as they tried to push their way through the crowds of people who were listening to him they became fascinated by what Jesus was saying and they forgot what they had been sent to do. Transfixed, they only wanted to listen to his words. Eventually they returned empty-handed to their bosses.

"Where is he?" they angrily asked the two men. "We sent you to bring him here."

The two men looked down at the ground and were embarrassed. "No one ever spoke like Jesus," was all they could say.

There was another wonderful storyteller whose name was Aesop. But unlike the Lord Jesus no one is really sure who he was. Many think that he was born on the shores of the Black Sea, 620 years before Jesus was born in Bethlehem. Others think that he was from Africa, maybe from Ethiopia. What we do know, however, is that he was a wonderful inventor of stories. When he died, they were gathered together and have been read and told ever since.

The apostle John tells us that Jesus Christ is "the true light that gives light to everyone" (John 1:9). Every person, man or woman, boy or girl, is made in the image of God. And even though that image has been damaged by our sin, like our creator God we are creative and able to sense beauty. We all have a conscience that tells us what is right and wrong, and all of us can see that it is foolish to live selfish, cruel and lazy lives. So, even though Aesop had never heard of the Lord Jesus, the apostle John teaches us that it was, in fact, the Lord Jesus that gave light to Aesop's stories.

This book is full of some of Aesop's most well-known stories. At the end of each tale is a short epilogue that teaches us something of the light that the Lord Jesus brings. My hope is that as you read them your lives and hearts will become illuminated with gospel joy and you will learn to love the Lord Jesus.

BELLING THE CAT

"Belling". What in the world does that mean? What a strange name for a cat. Did it have a black patch on its back that looked like a bell? How did it get *that* name? Oh, well "Belling" wasn't the name of this cat at all. Let me tell you how this word "Belling" came about.

The cat was actually called Tibby, and it was a great mouser. Each week, or so it seemed to its owner, it brought a dead mouse in through the cat flap. Its owner didn't like mice so even though the mouse always gave her a shock, she was happy that one had been caught.

You can imagine that the mice were not so happy, and after yet another of their family had disappeared through the cunning merciless cat, they held a council of war.

"Now what are we going to do about our great enemy? How are we going to stop it disappearing with our brothers and sisters?"

There was a long silence.

Finally a mouse said, "Couldn't we talk to it?"

There was laughter followed by groans.

"Talk to it? Talk to it? Any time it got anywhere near to us it would just want to kill us. Its nature is to destroy us. We could talk until the cows came home, but then when we had finished it would nod … and pounce on us and eat us!"

Then another mouse spoke, "There is that big dog who lives with the Smith family next door. Can't we persuade it to come here and finish off the cat?"

They thought about it for a moment until someone said, "That dog is as bad as that cat. If we went near it we wouldn't have an opportunity to say a word before it saw us. We would be running to the mousehole for our very lives."

"Anyway," someone else said, "as soon as the cat sees the dog coming it shoots up a tree and smiles down at it. It could never catch Tibby."

What could they do? They couldn't stay down under the floorboards; they had to forage for food.

Then a young mouse who had been listening with all the rest spoke up quite shyly. "Why don't we tie a bell around its neck? Then we could hear it coming and make our getaway."

Yes, that seemed a brilliant idea to everyone: belling the cat. It seemed an ideal solution that they would bell the cat. There was a quiet pause as they seemed to have found the answer they were looking for.

The silence was broken by one of the most respected of the mice. It cleared its throat and asked a question, "Ahem ... but who is going to bell the cat?" And they all looked at one another and hung their heads and knew it couldn't be done by even the bravest and strongest mouse. They were quite helpless to defeat their big, strong enemy. They just had to be very careful and look both ways when they came out of the mousehole.

———

Do you know that you have an enemy too? Your enemy is your sin. When you say, "Me, me, me!" and you want to be first and you won't let your brother or sister share and when you sulk because you can't have your own way and shout, "No, no, no!" at your parents—that is sin. Sin makes us miserable. It is our enemy and it does the same thing to every single person in the world.

So what can we do about it? We can know Jesus. He is the Son of God who died, was buried, rose again and was seen eating and drinking for almost six weeks before he went back to his Father in heaven. *This* living Jesus is more powerful than sin. He took the wrong things that we do, along with all their blame and shame, on himself on the cross. Instead of God being angry and punishing us, he charged his Son and judged him. Jesus accepted that judgement because he loves us and wants us to be with him for ever.

But God does something else as well: he puts a bell around our sin! When we say or do something sinful our consciences hear a sort of bell ring that says, "You shouldn't do that." Then we know that we are facing our enemy and we can ask God to give us strength to fight it. Every believer in Jesus can hear a bell that God has attached to all the sins that tempt us, and that bell rings out a message, saying, "Don't do it! Get away from it! Turn around and go back! I am here to protect you." The Lord Jesus has belled sin.

THE BOY WHO SHOUTED "WOLF!" BUT THERE WASN'T A WOLF

There was once a boy who was the youngest in his family. When he turned twelve he had to do what all of his brothers had done before him, he had to climb up the hill next to his house and keep watch over the flock of sheep who belonged to everyone in the village.

It wasn't long before the boy got bored sitting there all day long. There was nothing to do. All his friends were down the hill in the village having fun.

Then, one day, as he was looking across the valley to the edge of a wood he thought he saw a shadow in the trees. It looks like there's something moving down there, he thought. Afraid, he did what he was told to do, he stood on the edge of the hill, looked down over the village and shouted as loud as he could, "Wolf! There's a wolf! Wolf! Wolf! Wolf!"

Then to his satisfaction, he saw the blacksmith come out of his forge with his big hammer and begin to run towards him up the hill. After the blacksmith came his father and older brothers. Then the baker and the cobbler and the butcher and the old man with a beard who lived in a cabin down by the lake.

When they reached the top of the hill where the sheep were safely grazing they asked the boy where the wolf was. He pointed to the woods and they ran over carefully looking behind the trees and rocks. When they were sure the wolf had gone, the boy's father went back to his son and said, "Well done. You call us whenever you see the wolf again."

Peace returned to the village and soon the boy got bored again. What a lonely life he was living, he thought. No excitement. No fun. So a week later he went to the top of the hill overlooking the village and shouted again, "Wolf! Wolf! There's a wolf!"

This time, out came the candlemaker, the farmer, the carpenter and the wheelwright along with some of the others puffing and panting up the hill to the boy and the contented sheep.

"Where is it?" they shouted and the boy pointed to the trees again.

They walked in gingerly, close together, looking around, behind the trees and mounds of rocks, but there was no sign of the wolf. They nodded to the boy as they walked back down the hill.

The third time that the boy shouted "Wolf!" fewer villagers left their work to go up the hill. They no longer ran and this time didn't even ask the boy where the wolf was. In fact, they ignored him and strolled into the wood without even glancing at him.

That night his father asked him if he had been telling the truth.

"Of course," the boy said, wide-eyed in protest, embellishing the story by describing the wolf's great size and speed.

His father nodded silently while his brothers grinned to one another.

Another three weeks went by before the boy shouted "Wolf!" again. But this time there was a terror that raised the pitch and volume of his voice.

"Wolf! Wolf! Wolf! There's a huge wolf! Help!" he shouted because, he could hardly believe it himself, he could really see a wolf slinking around the edge of the woods.

The sheep saw it too and started running but the wolf was too quick and the boy could do nothing to stop the wolf killing the sheep one after the other. All the boy could do was shout, but the blacksmith stayed in his forge, the farmer kept ploughing his field, the candlemaker kept stirring his wax, the carpenter did not stop sawing and the old man with the beard who lived in the cabin by the lake didn't get up from his chair from which he was fishing. They all thought it was another false alarm. Others would go, they thought, but not them, they were not going to be made fools of for another wild goose chase. Who can blame them?

The Lord Jesus never shouted, "There's a wolf!" when there wasn't one. He only spoke the truth. One of the most important truths that he taught is that there are only two ways to live. One leads to everlasting life but the other leads to everlasting death. He wasn't telling lies when he said that. He wasn't like the boy shouting "Wolf!" and pretending there was danger when there wasn't really any. True danger really comes when we keep the Lord Jesus out of our lives. He wasn't shouting "Wolf!" when he warned us to be on our guard against the "false prophets who come to you in sheep's clothing but inwardly are ravaging wolves" (Matthew 7:15). Not everyone who tells you the way to heaven speaks the truth. Jesus said, "I am the way, the truth, and the life" (John 14:6). Always listen to the Lord Jesus. You can trust the warnings and promises that he makes. Safety and joy are found when we believe his words and trust in him.

ANDROCLES AND THE LION

In ancient times there was a slave named Androcles and he had had enough of being a slave. After another day in which his master had whipped him for not cleaning all the grease off the cutlery (even though he had been especially careful and had checked that every single spoon was shining) he decided he would run away. As his fellow slaves bound up his wounds, he told them what he planned to do, but they shook their heads.

"You know the penalty of being a runaway slave if you are caught?"

He nodded.

"You will be killed," said one.

"You will be thrown to the lions in the Coliseum," said another.

"Anything would be better than this wretched life," said Androcles.

So at midnight he climbed out of the window of the slaves' dormitory, and patted the heads of the guard dogs who licked his legs as he walked past them. He climbed up over the wall by a pile of boxes that he had left there that afternoon, and dropping down on the other side he ran as fast and as far as he could from that horrid master. He travelled during the night and slept in the woods during the day and soon had gone 100 miles.

One afternoon, hiding in the forest, he got up and was walking along a path when he turned a corner, and saw a lion. Androcles froze. All the strength went out of his legs and he stood petrified waiting for the lion to run and pounce on him and eat him. But the lion did not move, and as Androcles gazed at him in horror he noticed that the paw of the lion was very swollen. He could put no weight on it at all. He could not move. The lion was dying, and Androcles' horror turned to pity. He slowly moved towards him. The lion softly growled, but Androcles detected no threat in the sound. He got down and slowly crept right up to the lion and stroked his head and his healthy leg. All the time he was looking at the paw of the lion and there he spotted the end of a very large thorn that was buried deep in the lion's flesh. Androcles went down to the brook and folded a large leaf and filled it with water and brought it back to the lion. It was swallowed immediately. Then he went back for some more, and for some more, and more. Many times he brought water for the lion to drink until the animal was satisfied. Then he stroked the lion's wounded paw very, very gently. He finally took hold of the top of the thorn with a strong finger and thumb and, looking deep into the lion's eyes, he swiftly pulled the thorn out. The animal seemed to sigh and were there tears in his eyes? There were certainly tears in Androcles' eyes.

He stayed with the lion for days as the lion limped down to the stream and drank, and cooled his foot. Androcles made some traps and caught rabbits and gave the lion food. They eventually slept side-by-side and played together. But Androcles knew it couldn't last and he had to leave his friend. He wrapped his arms around the lion's great head and then walked away, far away, from the wretched place where he had been a slave.

Months went by and Androcles grew careless, taking his freedom for granted. One day he walked into a trap and found himself surrounded by a group of soldiers who tied him up and marched him to the local prison. He was accused of being a runaway slave, found guilty and condemned to death. The next day he was taken in a wagon with other runaways all the way to Rome and thrown into the horrid dungeons under the Coliseum. Four days later he heard the noise of crowds of people filling the Coliseum and the roars of hungry beasts that were being starved so that they would eat all the prisoners in the arena.

In the afternoon two soldiers hauled Androcles out of the dungeon and took him into the Coliseum to be greeted by the hoots and boos of the crowd. The soldiers put a rope around his waist and attached it to a stake. He could move a little way from the stake. That was all. The crowd shouted their greetings as the Roman Emperor and his family with governors and generals entered the imperial box. Then a great silence descended on the arena. Finally a portcullis was lifted at one of the sides and a gasp went up as a lion ran out snarling at the people and blinking in the unfamiliar sunlight. Then he saw Androcles at the stake and bounded towards him. The crowd went wild, until the lion stopped, and Androcles lifted up his head and gazed at the lion. The lion's tail began to wag and he bounded towards Androcles as the runaway slave smiled and lifted up his arms to embrace him. The lion licked him and licked him and

Androcles stroked him speaking gently to him, scratching his head and hugging it to his chest. The crowd's mood changed. There was first the lust for blood, and then the silence at the change in attitude of the lion, and finally great cheers and applause at the spectacle.

The emperor sent for Androcles. How did this man have such power over ferocious animals? Androcles told him their story of how they had become friends. The emperor was impressed and granted the runaway slave his freedom.

"What of my friend the lion?" asked Androcles.

"I shall keep him as my pet in the imperial zoo," announced the emperor, "no harm shall ever come to him."

"Do you need a keeper in the zoo?" asked Androcles.

The emperor laughed and slapped his thigh. "Yes I do," he said, adding, "you are hereby appointed the imperial lion keeper."

The crier stood before the multitudes that day and announced to them the whole story. There was great applause. It was the happiest gathering the Coliseum had ever seen.

One of the great titles that God has given to the Lord Jesus is that he is "the Lion of the tribe of Judah". He is awesome. He has all authority and power in heaven. All the angels obey his commands even though they are powerful and frightening creatures themselves. The apostle John once saw an angel on the Greek island of Patmos and the sight drained him of all his strength and he collapsed.

Immediately the angels spoke to him. "Get up! Don't worship me. Worship only God!"

The angels are holy and powerful and awesome, but what must their Creator and Lord be like?

We are all going to meet Jesus Christ one day. Are you afraid? If you have put your trust in him, then you don't need to be afraid because the Lion is your Saviour, and he has given his life for you. When we see him, the great Lion will take the form of a lamb and will run up to us and nuzzle his head against our body and smile at us. He has been waiting to see us for so long. This is Jesus our dear Saviour who delivers us from our slavery to sin and makes us members of his heavenly shepherd's flock for ever. No harm shall come upon us and nothing will ever separate us from the love of the Lion King of heaven.

THE DONKEY AND THE DACHSHUND

There was once a very rich farmer who had a pet dachshund he named Babs and a donkey he also liked that he called Doopy. But Doopy was more than a pet, he worked in the fields carrying tools to the farm workers and he brought water from the well in special containers on either side of his back. At the end of the day he was glad to get into his stall, and eat his oats and lie on his bed of hay and sleep all night. But how envious Doopy was of his friend Babs. One day at harvest time he was waiting to carry scythes and sickles out to the top of the great field when he looked through the window into the parlour and saw Babs the dachshund entertaining her master. She was chasing her tail and the master was laughing. Then she ran across the tiles and jumped up onto the master's lap. He hugged her and pushed his face into her warm back and stroked it.

All the way to the top of the great field carrying the tools, and then all the way back, Doopy was thinking about what he had seen.

"I wish I wasn't a donkey! Why can't I be a pretty little dog!"

As he walked he thought of how he could get closer to his master and make him love him the way he loved Babs.

When he arrived back Doopy stood still for five minutes, and then he walked across to the front door of the farmhouse. He pushed the door open and walked in, up the corridor and into his master's room. His master looked up as he heard the clippety clop of Doopy's hooves on the wooden floor. Then Doopy started to chase his tail; round and round he ran, knocking into the little table and hitting over a pedestal with a bowl of flowers. His master was very alarmed and his servants had never seen anything like it. Then Doopy ran up to his master and jumped up onto his lap and started to lick his face with its long wet tongue.

"Get him off me!" he shouted at his servants.

And they all ran to Doopy and grabbed his long ears and put their arms around his neck, and pulled his tail over his back and manhandled the puzzled donkey out of the house. They picked up sticks and beat it, and pushed it into his stall. No oats that night. Doopy was very sore from the beating and he couldn't sleep. What had he done wrong? He had only done what Babs did and Babs got kisses and laughter. What a cruel world it was!

God has created everything to be different. No two leaves are alike, and no two blades of grass are the same. It's not surprising that God makes every person to be unique, too. There is no one else just like you. You may have brothers or sisters but you are probably quite different from them, even though you have the same parents. Sometimes, though, we want to be like other people. Maybe you wish you were more clever, or you wish you were a different size, or you wish you had different coloured hair. But God has made you different from others. Be content with how God has made you. Doopy was foolish to want to be Babs. Doopy could do what Babs could never do. Doopy was indispensable on the farm in a way that Babs was not. So you are needed just the way you are.

God gives each of us his love. If we trust in him

then he gives us a new heart and the main feature of that heart is that it loves others. This is what makes us the same as other Christians, but God also gives us different gifts to make us different from each other. It is the gifts that God has given to us that make us unique and special. It can be so tempting to want to copy other people and be like them but we should ask God to help us to be the person that he wants us to be. Look at the trouble the donkey got into when he began to behave like a dachshund. Be yourself by the mighty love of God. Then you will start to discover your own joy in living the Christian life by the help of the Lord Jesus, just the way you are.

THE COWARDLY BAT

The animals and the birds were going through a very unhappy time. The animals were complaining about the birds dirtying the trees and the fields, and the birds were complaining about some of the animals stealing their eggs and eating their chicks. They both got more and more angry and called each other names, and in the end the birds declared war on the animals and the animals responded by declaring war on the birds.

The birds were the first to approach the bat and they said to him, "You will fight for us won't you? You are so fast and so hard to catch. You can fly from side to side, diving and soaring. You'll dodge anything the monkeys throw. You can be our messenger. We will make you our Messenger Captain."

But the bat shook his head. "You honour me, but I really can't fight on your side. I have no feathers, and I can't whistle and sing as you birds can. I don't lay eggs. I'm not really a bird. Sorry." And with those words he flew away.

Then it was the turn of the animals to approach the bat. They said to him, "You will fight for us won't you? You are quick, no one can catch you, and we need spies to mix with the birds and find out what their plans are, where and how they plan to bomb us, and where their headquarters are. We will make you Spymaster General."

The bat hung his head, "But you see I don't belong to you. I have wings and I fly in the sky. I roost high in the old church tower. My feet never touch the ground. I could not fight for you. Sorry." And with those words he flew away and disappeared.

This war—if you can call it a war—was over before it began. The birds could not conquer the ground and the animals could not conquer the air and though they roared and squawked and crowed and hissed at one another not one bird or animal was hurt. So after three days the leaders of the birds and the leaders of the animals met together and called a truce.

"We will end this war today," they said and quietly

went back to doing what they always did, looking for food for themselves and their little ones.

The bat was delighted that the war was over and he flew to the birds to say how glad he was that peace was restored. Many birds flew away when they saw him coming towards them, and they turned their backs and talked among themselves.

"Hello!" the bat cried with a grin on his face. "Hello! It's me. Hello! I just came by to tell you how glad I am that the war is over." They would not even look at him.

"Go away coward," they shouted. "You would not join us in fighting against those who steal our eggs and kill our young. You didn't want to know us then, and we don't want to know you now." They all ignored him and off he flew, all alone.

The bat then went down to hang out with the animals, but they all turned their backs on him too.

"Hello! Hello!" he shouted, but they acted as if they hadn't heard a thing. "Hello! It's me," the bat cried and kept crying.

"Go away. Go away coward! We asked for your help against those who swoop down and eat the dormice and voles and fish and little lambs. But you would not help us. You said you did not belong to us

23

GEOFFREY THOMAS

because you had wings and could fly. Okay. Then fly away and don't come back!"

Up, up and away he flew, rejected by both birds and animals he faced a lonely future. That was the fruit of being a coward.

There are times in our lives when we have to choose and take a stand. The Lord Jesus said, "If you decide that you are not for me, and don't believe and do the things I say, then you are against me." Imagine that! Jesus also said that it was impossible for anybody to serve two different masters. Imagine being told by one master to go to school and by another to go out and get a job. It is impossible to please both. If you go to school you are not going to work. If you go to work you are not in school. You cannot please two different masters who have two different plans. You can only serve one. And whichever one you choose reveals who you think is your real master.

We have to choose between doing what Satan tells us to do and what Jesus wants from us. There was once a writer called John Bunyan who wrote a famous book called *The Pilgrim's Progress*. There's a character in the book who always tried to please good as well as

24

evil. John Bunyan called him "Mr. Facing Both Ways". And do you know what happens to people who act like him? No one likes them. Nobody admires people who say one thing and then do another. It's easy to follow Jesus when it's the popular thing to do, at summer camps and big conferences, but when you see hard times coming, do you stick with Jesus or do you behave as if he didn't rise from the dead?

There's a hymn which starts, "Who is on the Lord's side? Who will serve the King?" Will you say with your lips and believe in your heart these words, "As for me, I will always be on the Lord's side"? And will you behave as those who serve Jesus as Master and King of kings? If you do, God will give you the courage to confess him as Lord.

THE BATTLE BETWEEN THE SUN AND THE EAST WIND

The east wind and the sun were having an argument as to which of them was most powerful.

The wind said, "I am more powerful than you. I can drive great windmills that make electricity that lights up cities. I can drive huge sailing boats all the way around the world. I can support gliders that fly across the sky for miles."

The old sun smiled and agreed that the wind could do all those things. "But let's be practical," he said. "See that hiker there climbing up Mount Snowdon? See how he is wearing that long coat? Which of us can remove it from him?"

"Agreed!" said the east wind relishing a competition. "When can we start?"

"Right now," said the sun.

"Okay," said the wind, thinking how easy this was going to be, and began to blow and blow at the hiker, almost knocking him off his feet. The coat was almost off his shoulders and flapping around his back, so the wind blew harder. But what did the man do? He tightened his belt, and did every button up, right to the top, and put his left arm close to his body and held on to his coat while he leant on the stick he was carrying in his right hand. Try as best as he could, the wind totally failed to remove the hiker's coat. In fact the man found a big rock and lay behind it in his coat to protect himself from the icy blasts from the east wind. When he did that, the wind knew he had failed.

"Now it's my turn," said the sun, and he started to shine on the rock and the man lying down behind it. The man began to unbutton his coat, first the top button and then the next and the next until he had unbuttoned the coat. Still the sun shone on the man and he began to sweat. Finally he was boiling, and so he got up and took off his coat and draped it over his arm as he walked in the sunshine up Mount Snowdon.

The sun smiled to himself, and the east wind told him, "You were certainly more powerful than me in removing that traveller's coat."

The sun said to him, "Let me tell you a story." And he did.

"One day a fox was walking through the wood when he looked up and saw a crow sitting on a branch with a large piece of cheese in its beak.

'Mmmm,' thought the fox. 'There's my supper.'

He looked up at the crow who saw him there and the bird took a firmer grip on the cheese between his teeth.

'Hello dear crow,' said the fox, 'I have watched you for so many years and admire you so much. You are looking well today. Your feathers are shining in the sun. Are you keeping well?'

The crow thought that the cunning fox was up to something and so he said nothing, just nodded his head in response to the fox's words. He kept a firm grip on the lump of cheese.

Then the cunning fox spoke again, 'I love to walk through the forest and listen to the birds singing. Some animals think that the nightingale has the sweetest song. Others just pause and listen to hear the lark ascending and its music is their favourite. Others say that the blackbird is the most delightful singer of all the birds. But do you know who is my favourite?'

29

The fox paused for effect as if he was waiting for the crow to answer.

'Yes. It is you crow. We all get so excited when you sing with that glorious tenor voice of yours. I could hear you all day. I think the very trees tremble with delight when they hear you singing.'

The crow wriggled with pleasure at the flattery and opened his mouth to sing, and immediately the cheese dropped down from the tree and landed near the fox. He pounced on it and swallowed it. The poor vain crow looked down in frustration, thinking of how he had been fooled by the flattery of the fox."

The sun finished telling the east wind the story and added, "Do you see how a bit of flattery will get people to do things that threats and power will fail to do? Warm their hearts and breathe sweetly to them with encouraging words, and soon they will be eating out of your hand and doing anything you wish."

Dr. Luke wrote the fifth book in the New Testament, the book of Acts, and in it he writes about cruel King Herod who was very angry with the people of Tyre and Sidon because they had insulted him. But they needed food from the king's lands, and so when he spoke to them in a big meeting they all shouted out a rehearsed response and worshipped Herod, "The voice of a god and not a man! The voice of a god and not a man! The voice of a god and not a man!" They were actually telling him what the king thought of himself. So instead of him saying to them, "Silence! Don't be silly. That is blasphemy. Only the Lord is God. I am a mere man and a sinful man at that," he instead twitched with delight, and took the flattery to his heart and soaked up the worship with pleasure. But the only Lord of lords, who is King over heaven and earth, was angry with people calling a man, who happened to be a very cruel man, a god. And so, soon the flattered king died. Flattery can destroy people.

It doesn't take us long to learn that if we flatter people we can get our way. People who want you on their side will also flatter you. They might not be Christians, but they like you and want you to change, and so they tell you how much they admire your belief in God, they say nice things, and hearing them can make you strut like a turkey. Beware of being bought by smiles. The Lord Jesus never flattered people. He didn't flatter his closest friends, and he certainly didn't flatter the most "important" people of his day, the Pharisees. He could have won them over by complimenting them but instead he told them the truth about themselves even though it hurt to hear it.

The apostle Paul wrote a letter to the Christians in Rome and he warned them of people coming into the church who wanted to destroy it. How would they do it? He told them, "They deceive the hearts of the unsuspecting with smooth talk and flattering words" (Romans 16:18). Remember the power of flattery to change us because if not we may lose our trust in Jesus Christ.

TO LIVE AS A SWAN OR A PEACOCK YOU MUST BE BORN AS A SWAN OR A PEACOCK

There were once two very restless, birds, one was a raven and the other was a crow. Let me tell you first about the raven. Her nest was high in the trees near the river and she looked down on the swans as they swam up and down and put their long necks into the river and ate fish and frogs. What beautiful birds they were. As she grew up and began to fly over the river she began to envy the swans. If I did what they did I would become a swan myself, she thought. So she started to splash in the river day after day, but her feathers remained as black as coal and didn't change white like the swans'. She tried to paddle but she had claws rather than webbed feet and so she couldn't move through the water and was carried along by the river while the other birds laughed at her. She couldn't dive into the water and so never caught a fish, and when she tried to swallow the weeds along the river bank that the swans devoured, they stuck in her throat, and she got stomach ache and grew thinner and thinner. Finally the raven died and her body floated downstream into the sea.

Now let me tell you about the carrion crow. He was perched on an old oak tree in a field when out of the corner of his eye he noticed an eagle soaring overhead. Suddenly the eagle swooped down and landed on the back of a little lamb, grasping it with its talons, and spreading its mighty wings, it went up and up into the air flying the lamb to his nest as food for his hungry chicks. The carrion crow was very impressed.

"Now that is a real bird," he said to himself. "I will be like that. I can do that."

And so he leaped into the air and flew across the field over the sheep, saying to himself, "You can do it. Yes. You can do it. You can do it." So he swooped down onto the back of Billy the ram, the father of all the lambs in that flock. Then he flapped his wings furiously, up down up down up down up down. But he stayed exactly where he was. The crow and the ram did not rise up from the ground even one inch, in fact the old ram hardly noticed that the carrion crow was on its back.

"Whew!" The crow paused for breath. "I am too weak, and this ram is too heavy. I will have to stick to eating the animals that cars have hit and killed on the side of the roads. Yuk!"

Then he decided to fly back to his perch on the old oak tree. But he couldn't. Try as he might his claws were tangled in the thick fleece of the ram. He flapped his wings again and again, up down up down up down. He seemed to be glued to the back of the old ram, who all the time seemed to feel no weight, and heard no flapping noises.

In the next hour the shepherd came along and looked over the field. He counted the lambs. One was missing!

"Has the fox got one, or has that eagle taken it?" he said, and was cross.

Then he noticed the carrion crow perching on the back of the ram, the daddy of the flock. How strange! He walked towards the animal and the bird on its back fluttered his wings, and did so more furiously as the shepherd got nearer.

"Well, well! What have we here?" said the old shepherd. "That rascal has his claws tangled in Billy's fleece."

The frightened crow was desperate in his attempts to get away. The shepherd came up to the ram and grabbed him and tore him off the ram's back. He brought it home and clipped his wings with scissors and put him in an old cage that had been in the shed for years. When the children came home from school they were fascinated to see the strange bird in the cage.

"Daddy, Daddy, what a funny bird! What is it?"

"It's only a carrion crow, and I have him here until the lambs are fully grown. He won't be pecking any of their eyes out this lambing time. I will let him go when they have grown. Yes, he's just a crow, but if you asked him what he is, he would tell you 'I'm a golden eagle!'"

There is only one way that a black raven could become a white swan, and that is by being born a swan. And there is just one way that a carrion crow could become a golden eagle, and that is by coming out of the egg of a golden eagle, with parents that are golden eagles. There is no other way. Behaving like swans will never make a raven a swan. Eating what they eat and trying to sound like them, and doing what they do will never change who you are. If you are born a carrion crow then you will be a carrion crow for the rest of your life. If you are born a raven then that has to be your future. If you are to become a real child of God so that he becomes your heavenly Father and you can speak to him any time and call him, "Abba! Father!" then he must give you a birth that comes from heaven. That's what we call a new birth.

A good man whose name was Nicodemus once came at night to talk to Jesus. He admired Jesus and believed that he had come from God. That could be the only explanation for his wonderful life, Nicodemus thought. He could see it in the way that Jesus taught others. He spoke like no one else. Nicodemus could also see the extraordinary power that Jesus had over disease, demons, death and the creation itself. Nicodemus was absolutely right, of course.

But Jesus did not shake hands with him and say, "Well done. You are thinking along the right lines. I have come from God and he is with me." In fact the Lord Jesus told Nicodemus, "You must be born again."

Nicodemus didn't understand at first. Even though he lived a good life and he knew that Jesus came from

God, it wasn't enough to take him to heaven. He needed a divine change in his heart and life.

Every single person who receives Jesus Christ into their life is given the wonderful privilege of becoming a new creation and a child of God. What a change! When this happens all our past, present and future sins are pardoned. Christ's righteousness is given to us and we are adopted into God's family. We become united to Jesus and our future home is changed; we have a place in heaven reserved for us. "This is yours," God says, "and no one else's." Just like there are parking places reserved for someone's car and no one else can park there, God has a place in heaven for everyone who is born again.

The carrion crow could not become a golden eagle unless he was born an eagle. The raven could not become a swan unless she was born a swan. A person cannot become a child of God unless he or she is given another birth by God. So what can you do? Pray to God and say, "Please Father, make me your child. Give me a birth from heaven. Make me a new creation. Change me and forgive all my sins, through Jesus Christ. I can't make myself your child. You must do it." And when you pray like that, and you really mean it, then God will give you the privilege of becoming one of his children.

THE LAST DAYS OF THE OLD LION

The lion was growing old, his teeth were worn and yellow, he panted for breath, and his enemies gloated fearlessly at his evident decline. The warthog actually charged him to try and crack his ribs. The zebra came up to him and kicked him from behind. Can you believe it? The gnu tried to spear him. The buffalo butted him. In fact all of his old enemies did everything in their power to starve him to death. The little animals had been safer when the lion ruled because he never bothered them. Now no one was safe. There was no law in the jungle. No one to protect the weak or punish the evildoer.

But even though the lion was weak, he had lost none of his cunning—and he was hungry. He retired to his cave where some of his friends came to visit him.

"Hello," he said feebly as they entered the cave. "How kind of you to call. Come in. Come close because I am quite hard of hearing."

So the days went by, and then the fox called by, "Hello Lion, how are you today?"

"Ah, who is that ... my eyesight is very poor these days."

"It's me, Fox."

"Ah, so nice to see you old friend. Thank you for stopping by. Come a little closer could you? I can't see you very well."

"How is the family?" said Fox, ignoring the invitation to come into the cave and close to the lion.

"Oh them," said the lion. "You know that I never see them these days. That is why it is so good of you to call by. Could you come a little nearer for me to see your face?"

Again the fox ignored the invitation and said, "Is there anything I can get you?"

"No, nothing at all dear old friend. But could you just come up to the bed so that I can really hear you. I am getting deaf in my old age."

There was a long silence and the fox didn't move from the doorway.

"Why is it," said the lion irritably, "that you stay all the way over there and won't come closer for me to see and hear you?"

There was another long pause.

Finally the fox spoke, "Well, this is the reason. All the footsteps on the cave floor go towards you and your bed. None of them show that your friends actually walked out of your home. Good morning, old lion."

And with that the fox walked away from the cave.

In the Old Testament, there was a great prophet named Jeremiah who spoke a lot about God's promised saving-King, Jesus Christ. And he once asked the people he was speaking to if it was possible for a leopard to change its spots. The answer is obvious. Even if the leopard washed itself in a lake with all its effort it could never lose its spots. It's the same with us. We are sinful by nature and it doesn't matter what we try to do, we just cannot change our sinful hearts. It is God who must give us new hearts. There's a famous old hymn by a man called Charles Wesley that says:

O for a heart to praise my God, a heart from
  sin set free;
A heart that's sprinkled with the blood so
  freely shed for me.
A heart in every thought renewed and full of
  love divine,
Perfect and right and pure and good, a copy,
  Lord, of thine.

Wouldn't it be awful to grow old like the lion in the story, and be weak and bullied and mocked but still be a liar and a killer? Don't grow old with a heart that is ruled by sin. Ask God to give you a new heart where Jesus Christ is in charge. Millions and millions of people have asked God to give them this heart, and he has answered every one. Don't think for a moment that he will ignore you if you ask him to take away your sinful heart and replace it with a pure, clean heart.

THE DONKEY AND THE STATUE

Do you remember the story that I told earlier about the donkey that was jealous of the dog that his master loved, and how he tried to behave like the puppy and jump up onto the lap of his master? He was soundly beaten for his folly and then sold to a carrier man who used him to take loads across rivers and mountains. This donkey never learned. Let me tell you what happened one day: they were going across a river and he was carrying two sacks of salt, but his feet slipped on the rocks at the bottom of the river and he fell in and struggled to get back on his feet. The carrier man pulled him up and they finally got to the other side of the river. When he got up on the bank, the donkey realised that the water in the river had dissolved a lot of the salt and his load was much lighter. So the next time he crossed the river he pretended to slip and he fell under the water again. This time his master was angry with him, but the donkey did not learn. The next load he carried in two sacks were sponges.—you know when you have a bath you use a soft sponge to rub over your body—the silly donkey got halfway across the river and pretended to fall in again and his carrier man did nothing to stop him. When he got to his feet and came out on the other side of the river the donkey staggered at the new weight of all the sponges. They had absorbed gallons of water, and for the rest of the journey to the shopkeeper's premises he had to carry a much heavier load.

His master was very patient with him and did not sell him until one day they were going down a mountain and the path was very steep. The donkey looked over the side of the path and the bottom of the mountain seemed very near. Why zig-zag across the side of the mountain when you could go straight down? The donkey tried to jump off the edge of the path but the carrier man hung onto his tail and pulled him back from the edge. But there was never a more stubborn donkey so that later, when his master was looking another way, the donkey jumped right off the edge of the path and tumbled over and over down the rocky hillside. He bounced from one rock to another, from one painful thorn-bush to a cactus plant. Wham! Bang! Ouch! Ooh! Ah! Ow! Oh! He hit his jaw. He scratched his legs. He smashed his nose into the trunk of a tree. He cut his knees. He caught his tail between two large rocks. Finally he landed on his back on a boulder at the side of the river, trembling and groaning. That is where his master found him half an hour later. He shook his head and looked at this silly animal, and said quietly, "Enough is enough." Then he took him to the animal market and sold him.

In the small town where the carrier man lived there was a temple. It was a wild place where monkeys lived on the roof and people from the town went to make offerings to an idol who frightened them. The idol was a large statue in the middle of the temple. It was very ugly and had six arms and two heads, with one eye in the middle of each forehead. The priests who ran the temple needed a donkey to help with their work and so they bought the donkey from the carrier man.

Once a year there was a special temple procession. The statue was put on the back of the donkey and paraded around the town. All the priests walked behind it chanting how great their ugly idol was. People threw flowers across the dusty road and cheered the donkey as it walked past. This made the donkey very excited. He loved the singing and he wanted to hear more and more of it. So he began to dance as he walked along. Clippety clippety, clop to the right, and clippety, clippety, clop to the left. Clop, clop, clop. Clip! Clop, clop, clop. Clip! And then he started to bray. Clipetty, clipetty, clop. Bray! Clipetty, clipetty, clop. Bray! Clipetty, clipetty, clop. Bray!

Those who were watching in the crowd laughed. But the priests who were walking behind the donkey got very angry.

"What does he think he's doing?" they said to each other and they ran with their sticks up to the donkey and began to hit his back. "What do you think you are doing? The crowds are not standing in the street and cheering because of you. They are cheering because of our idol that you are carrying. Behave! Be quiet! Stop braying! Stop dancing!"

And so the quiet donkey hung his head and walked back to the temple and to his stable and said to himself, "I won't be here for much longer. I wonder who my next master will be?"

Christians have one master, and it is Jesus. He is a wonderfully loving Lord. When he lived on earth he lived alongside twelve close followers and he showed them tremendous love. He was patient with them when they grew angry with other people, or when they argued with him, or even when they wanted to be number one in the world. He forgave them and continued to teach them and give them strength and energy to do all the things that showed others that they were his disciples. He gave them energy to forgive, and to love their enemies, and pray for them. He showed them that they ought to care for other people not just for themselves. He did this by getting on his knees one day and washing the feet of every one of them. He also did it when he went to the cross to die for their sins. He taught them that life was not about "Me, Me, Me," but about loving other people just as much as you love yourself.

Jesus not only tells us to live like this now but he sends his Spirit to help us too. The foolish donkey always wanted to give in to his feelings and to choose the easy way. He did not understand that the best way was to do what his master asked him and to do it with a happy heart. That is how we live a life that pleases

God. And a life that pleases God is the very happiest of all lives. Why not pray and ask God to help you? You could say, "Help me to do your will and obey you today, loving Saviour." Keep praying this as God keeps answering you.

THE BUNDLE OF STICKS

There was once a Christian teacher who ran a youth group at his church. Each week a group of boys would walk to the church from their homes in the town and make their way down the old stone steps that led to the basement. During the course of the evening the teacher would spend time trying to explain to the boys why Jesus came into the world. The boys would listen for a bit but most of the time they would just want the teacher to stop talking so they could have popcorn and lemonade and play games.

"Let me ask you a question," the teacher said to them one evening. "What is God like?"

The boys knew the answer. That was easy.

"God is love," one of them said very quickly,

hoping that the sooner he answered the question the sooner he'd be eating popcorn.

The teacher knew what they were thinking so he asked again, "What else is God like?"

There was a long silence and the boys wriggled.

"Let me write that down on this lollipop stick," the teacher said.

He took out of a packet a clean flat sticks and then he took his black felt pen out of his pocket and wrote on the stick in large writing GOD IS LOVE. The boys watched quietly.

"How strong is this stick?" he asked them.

They looked at him slightly confused.

"Could you break this stick?"

"Of course," they said.

The teacher gave the stick to the boy who had answered his first question and told him to snap it. The boy looked at him and snapped it easily.

"Let me tell you something more about God," the teacher said. "GOD IS LIGHT. There is no darkness, no sin in him at all. He is a holy God. Let me put that on a stick. Oh yes, and I had better write down the first thing you told me once again, GOD IS LOVE."

He was soon done and put the two sticks down.

"Now let me say something else about God, there is one God. The Father is God. The Son is God. The

Holy Spirit is God and these three are one God. I had better write that down hadn't I?"

So he took a new stick out of the packet and wrote on it with his felt pen, THERE IS ONE GOD.

"Now let me tell you something else about God, THE FATHER SENT THE SON TO BE THE SAVIOUR." He then told them a verse from the Bible, "For God loved the world in this way: He gave his one and only Son, so that everyone who believes in him will not perish but have eternal life." Before saying, "That is the reason why Jesus, the Son of God, came into the world."

Then he wrote those words on another lollipop stick.

"Now let me tell you more about why Jesus came into the world." He paused for a second to check they were all listening and then he said, "HE CAME TO GIVE HIS LIFE AS A RANSOM FOR MANY."

And he also wrote that down carefully on another stick, and then he told them that the Lord Jesus had once said that he did not come all the way from his throne in heaven in order to be served by people but, in fact, he came to serve others and, most of all, to give his life as the ransom that pays our debt and buys our forgiveness.

"That is so important I want to make it clear to you."

He took up another stick and he wrote on it, CHRIST DIED FOR OUR SINS. And he told the boys that everyone deserves eternal death because every single person rebels against God and ignores him but because Jesus Christ loved us so much he was willing to lay down his life as a sacrifice for our guilt.

"Do you know how God showed that he was completely satisfied with Jesus' death at Calvary?" the teacher said.

The boys looked at each other. Still silent and still longing for popcorn but now interested to hear a little more.

The teacher continued, "God raised him from the dead. Three days after he died, some women who followed Jesus went to his grave to make sure that his body was properly buried. But when they got there the huge stone that protected the tomb had been rolled away. Jesus was not there, only the clothes that he was buried in were left, neatly in a pile inside. Jesus had risen and he was alive and soon he came and spoke to one of the women in the garden where the graves were, and he also talked to two other men as they travelled along a road nearby. That evening he appeared to, and spoke with, his specially chosen disciples. He even had breakfast with them one morning on the beach. Later he also appeared to 500 other followers and spoke to them. It was an experience that those people never forgot and they talked about it for the rest of their lives. He stayed with his followers for almost six weeks and then ascended to heaven. So, let me write that down, THE LORD JESUS ROSE FROM THE DEAD. Do you know what that means?" he asked the boys finally.

They all shook their heads.

"It means that he is the most powerful person in the universe. It means that when we die we will meet the one who conquered death. So let me write down these words that describe the power Jesus has, ALL POWER IN HEAVEN AND EARTH. Do you know why you are here today? Because Jesus chose to bring you here to learn about him, and he chose you because he loves you. He wants you to hear about who he is and that he loved you so that you can become his disciple. I had better write that down on a stick."

Then he carefully wrote down those words.

"Now do you know where he is at this moment?"

One of the boys said, "In heaven?"

"Yes, in heaven, actually he is at the right hand of God. And do you know what he is doing there? He is praying for people like us. He is asking God that we trust and obey him. You know the chorus we sometimes sing, 'Trust and obey for there's no other way to be happy in Jesus but to trust and obey.' So let me write that down on this stick, JESUS PRAYS FOR HIS PEOPLE TO BE SAVED AND PROTECTED."

Then this fine teacher said to them, "One more thing. How do we receive Jesus Christ as our Saviour? We believe upon him. We put our trust in him. You've seen a little boy laughing when his father throws him into the air. He knows his father loves him and will catch him. He trusts his father not to hurt him. We trust our Lord to save us and keep us for ever. I had better write down that last word from God, BELIEVE ON THE LORD JESUS AND YOU WILL BE SAVED."

The teacher had now written God's word on ten sticks.

"How strong are these?" he asked the boys.

Then he got a roll of sticky tape and he taped them together.

"You could break one of those sticks, but can you break ten?"

He gave it to the same boy who had broken the one stick before. This time he struggled to break the bound sticks. He twisted them around in his hand

THE BOY WHO SHOUTED "WOLF!"

and screwed his face up as he tried but he could not break them.

"You could not break ten verses. Do you know how many verses there are in the whole Bible? There are over 31,000 verses and they are all inspired by God. In other words, they say exactly what God wants them to say to us. Jesus once said that Scripture cannot be broken. That heaven and the earth will pass away but not his word. The green grass of the summer will wither one day, and the petals will fall off the most beautiful flowers, but God's word never grows weak. The message of Jesus Christ will endure for ever."

The teacher was coming to the end of his talk but he wanted to make one final point.

"Do you see how important it is to learn as much about Jesus as you can? One verse about him will never make you strong, but the more you know about him the stronger you become. The reason I tell you these things is because I don't want you to be spiritual weaklings but spiritual strongmen. The more you know, the stronger you will be. Then you can be the type of person who helps others when they are feeling weak. So be strong in the Lord. That is the happiest life!"

How right that good teacher was.

REFORMATION LIGHTNING

We are a publisher specialising in creative Christian
writing for young readers.

Discover more at ReformationLightning.com